These doodles and scribbles belong to:

I began this journal on:

(date)

Authors: Tracy Molitors and Rita Cevasco
Illustration and Typesetting: Tracy Molitors
Website: www.rootedinlanguage.com

ISBN   978-0-9979031-3-3

Library of Congress Control Number   2017909333

Crooked Tree Press
Suite 350
7577 Central Parke Blvd.
Mason, OH 45040

Published in the United States

Explore-a-Story
Graphic Character Journal

Write

Draw

Think

Created by Tracy Molitors and Rita Cevasco

Getting the Most from Your Graphic Character Journal

Draw & Write for deeper insight!

Explore the books you read by creating a graphic of your favorite character. The word *graphic* refers to both writing and drawing—so let's call our creations *graphic characters*!

Start by selecting a character from a story. Each graphic you create will have it's own two-page spread in your journal. You have enough pages for 23 different characters from as many stories as you want.

There are five easy stages for creating a single graphic character. You can spread this over five days. Tracy provided fun examples which will help you add to your original drawing over time.

Working on each graphic in stages helps you dig in and relate to the story in a more personal way. Drawing will strengthen your writing, and writing will make your drawing come to life.

Throughout your journal, you will find tips and tricks to help with writing, drawing, and thinking. These pages are yellow, so they are easy to find.

Writing Tip: This journal is a place to gather thoughts about graphic characters. You can write full sentences or short ideas. Bits and pieces of writing can help you think of more things to say.

Drawing Tip: Your drawing skill isn't important. Focus on your character: imagine the features that make them who they are. Try starting with a stick figure—then add details to make your character more real.

Thinking Tip: By focusing on a character, you begin to notice little things you didn't see before. Exploring a graphic character uncovers the story's plot, conflict, and theme!

Write
Draw
Think

My c[...]

1.

CHOOSE YOUR
CHARACTER

My character acts . . .

Remember:

Drawing skill is
not important—just
thinking skill!

(date)

Character: _____

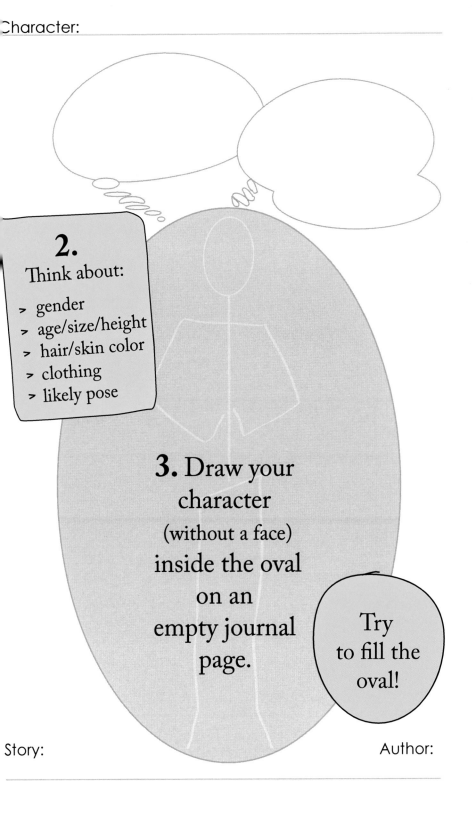

2.
Think about:

> gender
> age/size/height
> hair/skin color
> clothing
> likely pose

3. Draw your character (without a face) inside the oval on an empty journal page.

Try to fill the oval!

Story: _____   Author: _____

My character thinks . . .

1.

In the boxes, do some writing to describe your character's thoughts, feelings, and attitude.

Hint: It can help to think of a scene you like, and write about that scene.

My

(date)

STAGE THREE SUGGESTIONS:

My

Mulan often thinks

she's overlooked

Wants to he

shows her

alone. Sh

feeling u

Treats others fairly and cares

about them.

1.

Write your character's desire in the first thought bubble.

My character acts . . .

Courageou

rule-break

not above

her family

- Wants

- Fights

is n

2.

Write your character's main obstacle in the second thought bubble.

(date)

Character: Mulan

Story: Mulan
(Chinese folk character & Disney Movie)

Author:
Unknown

STAGE FOUR SUGGESTIONS:

Mulan often thinks she's overlooked.

Wants to hel...

shows her fe...

alone. She enj...

feeling useful. She ...

Treats others fairly and cares about them.

1.
Add a sign and write a message from your character.

My character acts . . .

Courageous and a ... honest, but ...ky to help ... her dad. ...he believes is right.

2.
Draw an item or symbol that is important to your character.

(date)

My character thinks . . .

Mulan often thinks she's overlooked. Wants to help. She shows her feelings alone. She enjoys feeling useful. She Treats others fairly and about them.

STAGE FIVE SUGGESTIONS:

1.

Fill in the background/ setting.

My character acts . . .

Courageous and a rule-breaker. She's honest, but not above being sneaky to help her family.

- Wants to protect her dad.

- Fights for what she believes is right.

(date)

My character

Mulan often thinks she's overlooked.

Wants to help. She only shows her feelings when she is alone. She enjoys learning and feeling useful. She hates bullying. Treats others fairly and cares about them.

My character acts . . .

Courageous and a rule-breaker. She's honest, but not above being sneaky to help her family.

- Wants to protect her dad.
- Fights for what she believes is right.

(date)

My character thinks . . .

My character acts . . .

(date)

My character thinks . . .

My character acts . . .

(date)

Character: _____

Story: _____   Author: _____

My character thinks . . .

My character acts . . .

(date)

My character thinks . . .

_____

_____

_____

_____

_____

_____

_____

_____

My character acts . . .

_____

_____

_____

_____

_____

_____

_____

_____

(date)

Story: Author:

Drawing Tips for Stick Figures

Stick figures are easy to master and do a good job of representing us.

With only a few rules-of-thumb, your stick figures can look more realistic, giving you more confidence when drawing your characters.

1. How Tall Are We?

- The average man is eight heads tall. If you stacked eight heads on top of each other, the stack would be the same height as a man.
- The average woman is six to seven heads tall.
- Children vary based on their age.

2. Where Is Our Middle?

Another handy reference to keep in mind is the **half-way point** on a human figure. Many people automatically think that our belly buttons are halfway down our bodies, but this is not true! The half-way point is just below our hip bones. So on your stick figures the half-way point should be right about where the legs join the body.

Note the half-way marks on all three figures. Knowing this will help you keep the figure's legs and body in proportion to each other.

A Cartoonist Trick:

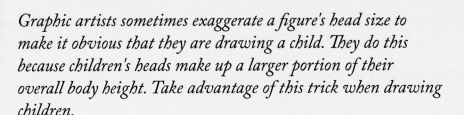

Graphic artists sometimes exaggerate a figure's head size to make it obvious that they are drawing a child. They do this because children's heads make up a larger portion of their overall body height. Take advantage of this trick when drawing children.

Write
Draw
Think

My character thinks . . .

My character acts . . .

(date)

Story: Author:

My character thinks . . .

My character acts . . .

(date)

My character thinks . . .

_____

_____

_____

_____

_____

_____

_____

_____

My character acts . . .

_____

_____

_____

_____

_____

_____

_____

_____

(date)

My character thinks . . .

My character acts . . .

(date)

Drawing Tips for Stick Figures

1. How Are We Built?

Adding just two horizontal lines—one for the shoulders and one for the hips—can make our stick figures more life-like.

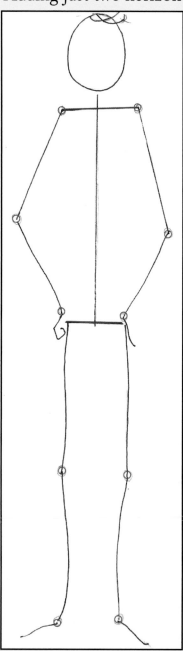

If you think about how we humans are built, you realize that our arms and legs don't come together in a point at our bodies. Instead our arms hang off our shoulders and our legs hang from our hips. With the addition of a line for shoulders and a line for hips, our stick figures suddenly look more real!

2. Where Do We Bend?

We bend in several convenient places that we call joints. If we add small circles to represent our major joints (shoulders, elbows, wrists, hips, knees, and ankles), this will help remind us where our stick figures can bend. Now we can start to move them around . . .

3. How Do We Move?

Stand up straight and picture yourself as a stick person. The lines of the stick person are the major bones of your body:

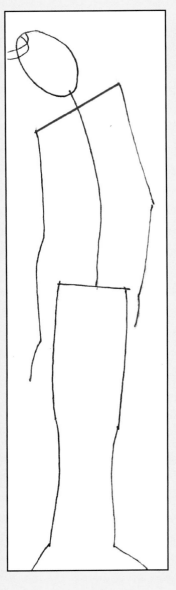

- Your spine runs up the center with your head at the top.
- Your shoulders cross your spine at the base of your neck.
- Your arm bones hang from your shoulders.
- Your hips cross at the bottom of your spine.
- Your legs extend down from your hips.

Now face forward and tip your shoulders to the right side. Feel what happens to your spine, shoulders, and arms. The vertical line that represents your spine is now curved like a banana.

The horizontal line that represents your shoulders is tipped, left end up high and the right end down low.

The left arm is now pulled up and the right arm has dropped. Your hips and legs are straight.

Since your head is attached to your spine, it naturally tips to the right along with your spine and neck.

Drawing Tips for Stick Figures

4. Practice Poses

Try drawing a stick figure that is bending to one side (see figure on previous page). Keep the legs and hip line straight, but curve the spine, tip the shoulder line, and make sure the arm lines follow the shoulder line. Remember: the arms are still the same length, but one will be higher up than the other.

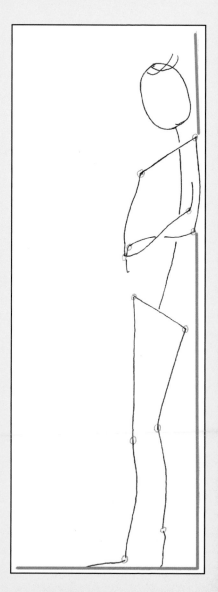

Now try other poses ...

Before you begin drawing, bend your own arms and legs and feel what the "bone lines" in your body are doing. Now draw a stick figure with "bone lines" in the same position.

As you get more comfortable thinking of your shoulders and hips as a line, you will be able to draw those lines on your graphics to show movement and position.

Use your own body to help you understand how to draw realistic movement with stick figures.

Go ahead, dive in—the more you play with drawing figures in different positions, the more expression you can give your characters!

Write
Draw
Think

My character thinks . . .

My character acts . . .

(date)

Character: _____

Story: _____   Author: _____

My character thinks . . .

My character acts . . .

(date)

Character: _____

Story: _____   Author: _____

My character thinks . . .

_____
_____
_____
_____
_____
_____
_____
_____
_____
_____
_____

My character acts . . .

_____
_____
_____
_____
_____
_____
_____
_____
_____
_____
_____

(date)

Character: _____

Story: _____   Author: _____

My character thinks . . .

My character acts . . .

(date)

Character: _____

Writing Tips for Symbols

Symbols are items or ideas in a story that stand for something more than just themselves.

For example, Mulan must climb a pole to become a warrior. The pole is a difficult test to prove her worthiness as a soldier, but it also symbolizes her need to prove her value to herself. Climbing the pole represents Mulan's self-confidence, proving she can succeed in a man's world.

All stories have symbols. Here are a few you may recognize: the sword or the round table in *King Arthur*, the ring in *The Lord of the Rings*, the suitcase in *Bud, Not Buddy*, the spider web or Pa's ax in *Charlotte's Web*, the golden ticket in *Willy Wonka and the Chocolate Factory*.

Thinking Tips for Symbols

Authors often use symbols to point to the themes of a story. If you spend time looking for a symbol in a story, and then think about why that symbol is important, you will discover one or more of the story's themes.

For instance, in *Mulan*, one of the themes is that people are worthy and capable, regardless of the prejudices against them. When you think about what the pole stands for, you realize it is a symbol of worthiness. The theme of the story is that even misfits are worthy and might even save the world!

Thinking Tips for Understanding Setting

Authors know they can't write about the whole world in a single story, so they make smaller worlds for their characters. Their smaller worlds represent our larger world. Sometimes the story's setting is a segment of our world, or sometimes the setting is a fantastical new world.

Think about how a character's world relates to the larger world around us. Ask yourself how their world is the same as ours. What tricks has the author used to make the character's world feel familiar to your own?

My character thinks . . .

My character acts . . .

(date)

Character: _____

Story: _____   Author: _____

My character thinks . . .

My character acts . . .

(date)

Character: _____

Story: _____   Author: _____

My character thinks . . .

My character acts . . .

(date)

Character: _____

Story: _____   Author: _____

My character thinks . . .

My character acts . . .

(date)

Character: _____

Story: _____   Author: _____

Drawing Tips for Details

1. Add Clothes

A great way to show details about your character is to draw what they might wear. This is easier than it sounds. Once you have drawn a stick figure for your character, imagine that the lines are bones. Now add clothes by tracing around the outside of the bones.

2. "Beef up" Your Character

Do the same thing with hands, feet, necks, or any other part of your character not covered by clothes. Draw around the outsides of the bones to add flesh or skin to your character. Use these clothes and skin lines to make your character as wide, round, or thin as you want!

3. Add Finishing Touches

Carefully choose colors for your character's clothes and skin.

Consider adding more details to your character, such as: hair style, hats, jewelry, or any other attributes that show your character's personality!

Thinking Tips for Details

Add clothes that "suit" your character's personality and setting. Think about the time period and look online to see clothes and hairstyles from that period. Find words to describe your character's personality and imagine how colors and details help express these ideas. Your character can hold beloved items or wear clothing that shows their place in the world.

Write
Draw
Think

My character thinks . . .

_____
_____
_____
_____
_____
_____
_____
_____
_____

My character acts . . .

_____
_____
_____
_____
_____
_____
_____
_____

(date)

Character: _____

Story: _____   Author: _____

My character thinks . . .

My character acts . . .

(date)

Character: _____

Story: _____   Author: _____

My character thinks . . .

My character acts . . .

(date)

Character: _____

Story: _____   Author: _____

My character thinks . . .

My character acts . . .

(date)

Character: _____

Story: _____ Author: _____

Drawing Tips for Facial Expressions

We communicate a lot of information with our faces—without using any words at all. We understand just by looking at someone whether they are pleased or upset, disappointed or excited. Imagine how much more we can show about our characters once we master how to add expression!

1. Placement of the Face

Because our eyes are so important, many people draw them at the top of the head. Surprisingly, our foreheads are bigger than most people realize. In fact our eyes are only about half-way up our heads. Using this fact, your character's face will be placed where it belongs on your character's head.

Correct placement of the face helps characters look more realistic. Therefore, draw your character's eyes around the halfway-point on the head. Then add the eyebrows, nose, and mouth based on your placement of the eyes.

2. Expressions

When making facial expressions graphically, we only have to change three lines to express nearly any emotion. The eyebrows and mouth say it all! To demonstrate this, examine the chart on the opposite page. The character's nose and eyes never change, yet the emotion changes in every square. See if you can label each expression!

Cartooning Expressions

Mouth \ Brows	Neutral Brows: — —	Brows curving up to center:	Brows slanting down to center:
Neutral Mouth: —			
Smiling Mouth: ⌣			
Frowning Mouth: ⌢			

Drawing Tips for Facial Expressions

3. Practice Making Faces

Here is the same chart to help you practice changing these three lines yourself—two eyebrows and one mouth.

Now practice different facial combinations on your own by looking in a mirror and imagining various feelings. Exaggerate your expression (as though you really want someone to get what you are feeling without having to say it). Figure out what direction your eyebrows and mouth are pulling for each emotion. Then exaggerate that expression even more on your practice paper to see what emotions you can convey in your drawing.

A Cartoonist Trick:
Many graphic artists prefer basic faces. Simple faces allow faster drawing, convey a certain style, and are easier to duplicate. Some artists make simple faces just because they are fun. Whatever the reason, facial features don't need to be complicated—people will still recognize and enjoy them!

Cartooning Expressions

Mouth \ Brows	Neutral Brows: ━ ━	Brows curving up to center: ◡◡	Brows slanting down to center: ╲╱
Neutral Mouth: ━			
Smiling Mouth: ◡			
Frowning Mouth: ◠			

Write
Draw
Think

My character thinks . . .

My character acts . . .

(date)

Character: _____

Story: _____   Author: _____

My character thinks . . .

_____
_____
_____
_____
_____
_____
_____
_____
_____

My character acts . . .

_____
_____
_____
_____
_____
_____
_____
_____

(date)

Character: _____

Story: _____   Author: _____

My character thinks . . .

My character acts . . .

(date)

Character: _____

Story: _____   Author: _____

*"Every story starts with an idea,
but it is the characters
that move this idea forward."*
—Michael Scott

Now that you have spent some time exploring, take a few moments to pick the most memorable characters who live within these pages. Write a note to yourself so you'll remember why these creations jumped off the pages and into your head!

Most Exciting Character:

Most Appealing Character:

Most Despicable Character:

12036886R00050

Made in the USA
Monee, IL
20 September 2019